Lead Mining
in the Yorkshire Dales

By Louise Maskill

Summerlodge East level

BRADWELL
BOOKS

1

Published by Bradwell Books
11 Orgreave Close Sheffield S13 9NP
Email: books@bradwellbooks.co.uk

1st Edition

ISBN: 9781912060948

Design by: Mark Titterton **Typeset by:** Mark Titterton **Print:** Gomer Press, Llandysul, Ceredigion SA44 4JL

Image Credits

Mark Titterton p.3, p.5 top-right, p.9, p.17, p.19 both, p.21 both

Karl Barton p.5 left, p.10 top and p.12 both iStock: back cover top-right, p.11, p.13, p.18, p.20, p.22, p.23, p.25, p.29 and p.31

Dales Countryside Museum p.1, p.6 and back cover, p.7, p.16 with kind permission of D Carlisle

D. Carlisle p.15 M. Samworth (Dales Countryside Museum) p.14 both

A special thank you to Dales Countryside Museum - Hawes

Dales Countryside Museum shares the fascinating stories of the people who have lived and worked in the Yorkshire Dales and have shaped this special landscape over thousands of years.

Housed in the former Victorian railway station at Hawes, the Museum is a great place to start a trip to the Dales. Discover the industrial heritage of the area, see the recently re-assembled Providence Mine water wheel and crushers and hear the stories of those who rescued it.

See the John Baker loco, climb aboard the carriages and get crafty in the Creation Station. There are loads of things to do all round the Museum. Have fun on our outdoor trail – take a woodland wander, see how many animals you can find and invent your own stories in our special storytelling chair!

As well as our galleries showcasing beautifully crafted objects like our Bronze Age spearhead and gold Viking ring, we also have a programme of special exhibitions that offer something new to see and a range of exciting events and activities, giving you the chance to roll up your sleeves and try something different!

dalescountrysidemuseum.org.uk

Contents

Introduction

The mining and working of metallic ores is one of the oldest industrial activities to be practised in the British Isles. From prehistory Britain was known to be rich in deposits of tin, copper, silver, gold, iron and lead, and over the centuries mining has underpinned the economies of many isolated and rural upland areas.

Lead mining in particular has always been a harsh, dangerous and often insecure existence, which shortened the lives of those who engaged in it and rarely resulted in fortunes for the men at the rock face. Nevertheless, whole communities were once dependent on lead mining and smelting, with the evidence of their activity to be found in the Yorkshire landscape to this day if one knows how and where to look for it.

Lead ore and the minerals associated with it typically occur in limestone country, less commonly in gritstone and occasionally in shale. Deposits of *galena* (lead sulphide) occur where hot fluids rich in mineral components migrated through the earth's crust, leaving behind them precipitates or traces of chemical reactions. Over millennia these traces built up to form veins, sometimes breaking the surface of the ground but often buried deep in caves or running through the rock.

In the limestone-rich hills of the Pennines the presence of lead ore has been known and exploited for thousands of years. The limestone, laid down by the mineral remains of creatures swimming in the shallow Carboniferous seas that covered the area some 310 million years ago, is interspersed with layers of shales and mineral ores, and capped by millstone grit at higher levels. It is no exaggeration to state that the detailed study of the UK's complex rock stratigraphy, often carried out prior to or during lead mining activities in the eighteenth and nineteenth centuries, kick-started the modern science of geology.

Galena is the world's primary source of lead. It occurs naturally in sedimentary rocks, and is metallic silver in colour when it is first exposed to the air, although it rapidly tarnishes to a dull grey. The maximum amount of lead which can be extracted from galena by smelting is around 86%, but few veins contain more than 10% galena; 5% is more likely, and any less means that extraction operations are likely to run at a loss if their chief target is lead.

However, galena is almost always found in association with various other minerals, chiefly sphalerite, fluorspar, barytes and calcite, and also with silver; in fact, many galena-mining operations today see these minerals or silver as their primary targets, with lead disregarded as a by-product. The extraction of the other minerals grew from the start of the twentieth century as the lead mining industry declined.

Each mineral has its own industrial uses. *Sphalerite* is the most important zinc ore, and is used in making galvanised iron, paint, and sometimes as a gemstone. *Fluorspar* is also used in jewellery

A galena sample

Galena with fluorite and dolomite

in the form of the prized Blue John (found near Castleton in Derbyshire), but it is also a source of fluorine for the chemical industry, and is used in the manufacture of Teflon, anaesthetics, toothpaste, aluminium and in the fluoridation of water. *Barytes* is used in paint manufacture, oil and gas drilling, and to make glossy paper for photographic printing and other uses, as well as in the barium meals used in modern medicine. *Calcite* is used to make pebbledash or stucco, in the paint for the white lines on roads, and for various purposes in the chemical industry.

Once, however, all these other minerals were regarded as waste products, with the search for lead driving the excavation of vast networks of shafts, caverns and tunnels beneath the Yorkshire landscape, as well as the construction of buildings and transport networks to process the extracted ore and ship the finished product. This book will take you on a tour of lead mining's history, the industrial uses of lead down the centuries, the methods used to extract and process the ore, and the locations of some of the most significant and picturesque remains to be found in the Yorkshire Dales.

Ruined buildings at Gunnerside

History of Lead Mining

The history of mining metallic ore in the Yorkshire Dales goes back thousands of years. The Romans knew of the presence of lead ore in the area; there are a number of known Roman sites, probably worked by open cast methods, along with evidence of roads and occupation. The discovery of *pigs* (ingots) of lead stamped with the names of Roman emperors allows them to be dated with some accuracy.

However, it is likely that lead was being mined in Britain long before the Roman conquest of AD43. The Roman historian Pliny wrote that the technique of *hushing* (damming watercourses and then allowing the water to sluice down hillsides, washing away topsoil to reveal vein heads) was known and practised by the pre-Roman Britons, so it seems likely that mining was taking place in the Dales long before the Romans arrived. There is also documented evidence of slaves working in mines in places such as Hurst in Swaledale and Greenhow Hill in Nidderdale around AD74 – perhaps the conquered local inhabitants who had been working these sites for generations, continuing under their new masters?

Richmond Station - loading lead pigs

Display at the Dales Countryside Museum featuring an original wooden wagon from Storey level, Greenhow

After the Roman departure the incoming Saxons and Danes continued to work lead in the Dales on a smaller scale. It is likely that many settlements in the Pennine uplands grew up around the mining industry rather than agriculture, with mineral rights often granted to the local lord of the manor by royal decree. The great Yorkshire religious houses also benefited from mining income on their extensive estates until they were divested of their possessions by King Henry VIII during the dissolution of the monasteries between 1536 and 1541. (It is ironic that the stripping of lead from the roofs of these once mighty religious buildings caused a glut in the lead market around this time.)

Henry granted the confiscated properties to his loyal noblemen, and some of these families went on to become influential in the local lead mining industry. Landowners typically claimed a royalty of somewhere between an eighth and a twelfth of any ore discovered, representing a valuable potential income on otherwise unproductive land. However, mining at this time was still on a relatively small scale, with the depth and extent of workings limited by the water table and the strength of men and horses to lift ore from deep underground.

Miners working on a small scale prospected for and worked mineral veins under a system of customary rights, bargains and duties. Mining in Yorkshire operated on a system of partnerships, with a small group of men (typically around six) striking a bargain with the landowner or company holding the mineral rights to work a particular area of a mine. The ore extracted by the partnership was brought from the mine and deposited in the partnership's own *bouseteam* – a stone-built hopper, rows of which can still be seen at some dressing and smelting sites today. The number of *bouseteams* outside a mine indicated its prosperity and the number of partnerships working within.

Accelerating industrialisation and improved technology (not least the increasing use of gunpowder for blasting) during the sixteenth and seventeenth centuries opened up new and deeper deposits and made mining and smelting more efficient, attracting investment from landowners, entrepreneurs and venture capitalists who sank (and sometimes lost) enormous sums of money in mining enterprises in the Dales.

This was a time of unprecedented prosperity and expansion in the mining industry nationwide. A petition to Parliament in 1642 listed some 20,000 people who were miners or otherwise involved in the mining industry. Improved drainage and ventilation techniques meant that water tables could be lowered and veins could be worked deeper without the risk of suffocation or drowning. However, miners working on a small scale were often driven from the best ore fields by powerful companies and forced to prospect in less profitable areas, or else they had to accept poorly-paid work for the larger outfits.

The eighteenth century saw the period of greatest industrial expansion, with large-scale capitalised mines operating alongside smaller family-owned or even one-man claims – a situation made possible by free-mining laws, according to which anyone could prospect for ore without hindrance from landowners, and could open a mine and retain the title to it as long as he continued to work it and could prove it was viable.

Lead mines in the Yorkshire Dales rarely reached the levels of industrialisation seen in other areas, due largely to their isolation and the inhospitable terrain. Water-driven machinery, notably wheels and pumps, did become common, however, meaning that previously flooded levels could be drained. The larger quantities of ore being raised led to new methods of transport and haulage underground. *Corves* (wooden sledges with iron runners) were hauled along wooden plankways, but these were soon replaced by wheeled carts, and then by wagons on iron rails. Occasionally water was used for underground transport, with boats moving ore and waste rock along natural streams or waterlogged levels; Stone's Level, in Little Punchard Gill in Arkengarthdale, was driven specifically as a canal level so that ore could be floated out of the mine. Horse levels were common in the Northern Pennine ore fields, with wide passages along which wagons could be drawn into and out of the mines by the local Dales Galloway ponies.

The industry went into decline after the late eighteenth century because of worked out veins and the increased excavation and maintenance costs of the deeper, more industrialised mines. In addition, the market became flooded with cheap imported supplies; import duties had protected the domestic industry for a few decades, but these were abolished in 1845. There were some investments during this period – a few mines had steam-driven engines installed for pumping water – but the expense was often ruinous for comparatively little return; a huge amount of investment was withdrawn around this time, and the industry declined rapidly.

The miners of the Dales had to find alternative employment when the lead mines closed, and many moved away to do so. Some went north to the Durham coalfields, some to the textile mills in the expanding industrial towns of Lancashire and Yorkshire, and some further afield to try their luck in the New World. In some areas of the Dales the depopulation that occurred with the extinction of the lead mining industry has never been recovered.

There were some hold-outs – the mines in the Arkengarthdale area continued in production after many others had closed, with the Faggergill mine still being worked in 1912. By the Great War, however, lead mining in the Yorkshire Dales had all but ceased.

Buildings at the Old Gang Smelt Mill

Uses of Lead Through Time

Historically, the lead from Yorkshire and elsewhere has found a wide variety of uses. From Roman times onwards much of the lead mined in the Dales made its way out of the area and a good deal was exported abroad; this continued until import duties were abolished in the nineteenth century, paving the way for cheaper foreign supplies to undercut local producers and sounding one of the death knells for the British lead mining industry.

A lead sundial

One of the earliest commercial uses of lead was in ancient Egypt, where black galena was used in the manufacture of the cosmetic kohl. This was applied around the eyes for fashionable purposes and because it was thought to reduce the glare of the desert sun, as well as repelling flies.

Cosmetic use of lead continued throughout the Middle Ages and into the eighteenth century, when white and red lead were used in products to whiten the skin or provide a blush. Queen Elizabeth I was an enthusiastic user of Venetian Ceruse, a white lead preparation for the face, and the fashion for pale skin with pink or red blush continued well into the eighteenth century. Unfortunately the prolonged use of these products causes inflammation, skin lesions, hair loss and eventually death from lead poisoning; it is telling that these side-effects were known for many centuries, but the use of lead in cosmetics continued.

A lead insurance plaque, indicating that the home owner had paid fire insurance

Lead is used in the manufacture of rechargeable batteries, particularly car batteries and units for use where large amounts of storage are needed, such as hospitals or mobile-phone masts. The chemical environment inside lead-based batteries is particularly noxious, being highly acidic and with a risk of

Lead roofing

explosion if gas builds up, but the recycling programme for the lead in these batteries is extremely successful and efficient.

Lead has many uses in the building industry. The smelted metal can be easily be formed into sheets which were used for external plaques or notices and in roofing, particularly in buildings such as churches or castles. Of course, this created a problem of theft, with audacious thieves stripping an entire roof of its lead and selling it on for scrap. This is by no means a historical issue; lead theft is once again on the increase, driven by rising scrap metal prices and increasing demand from developing economies.

In the military, bullets for rifles and other muzzle-loading firearms were moulded historically from pure lead. This works well because lead is extremely dense and provides a lot of kinetic energy when the bullet is fired, increasing the range of the gun. However, significant quantities of lead are deposited inside gun barrels during firing, causing a problem for the longevity of the firearm. Modern bullets are usually made of lead alloyed with tin, by using a lead core encased in a shell of steel or copper alloy. This reduces the deposits of lead inside gun barrels, without compromising on mass.

Lead is used in flashing for gutters and drains, for drainage finials, and in the construction of stained glass windows. Because of its malleability it can easily be moulded into pipes to carry both hot and cold water, as well as in solders; indeed, its use in this area was so common that the word *plumbing* derives from *plumbum*, the Latin name for lead. Once again, however, there are significant health hazards related to drinking water contaminated with lead, not least its tragic effects on stillbirth and infant mortality; it is now illegal to use lead pipes or solders in the supply of drinking water, although lead solders may still be used in closed systems such as central heating.

A lead finial

The paint industry was one of the main commercial users of lead, with different compounds giving red, yellow and white pigments. Lead may also be added to paint to accelerate drying, resist corrosion and damp, increase durability and maintain a fresh appearance, but as with all other domestic uses, it constitutes a significant health and environmental risk. Lead-based paint has been banned for domestic use in the UK since the 1960s, but many older houses may still have significant quantities of lead in old layers of paint.

Lead also found widespread use in the toy industry. White lead paint was used to decorate toys of all kinds, and die-cast lead models, for example soldiers or cars, were present in almost every family home. These toys have been banned for decades in much of the world, including Europe and the US, but lead is still used in toy manufacture in some developing countries, and these items can find their way onto international markets. It is also worth noting that lead is not banned in the manufacture of plastics, where it is used to increase flexibility and malleability, and these materials can still be used in toy manufacture.

Lead oxide has been used in glass manufacture for over three millennia, hardening the glass, making it easier to work and increasing its refractive properties. This type of glass was commonly known as crystal or lead crystal, although most of the modern crystal on sale for use with food or drink no longer contains significant quantities of lead because of its harmful health properties. Historically, however, lead crystal was highly valued because of its sparkling qualities and its distinctive ringing tone when tapped.

A lead toy soldier, with traces of paint

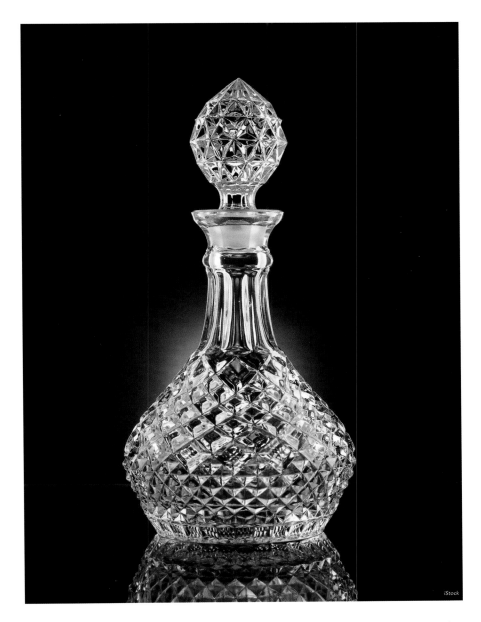

iStock

Finally, lead is still sometimes used in coffins. It was used by the Romans and throughout the Middle Ages in high-status burials, and it is still the tradition that members of the British royal family are interred in lead-lined coffins. As well as sealing the coffin, the lead was thought to have preservative properties – although this did not always work. Legend has it that when the corpulent King Henry VIII died in 1547 he was placed in a massive lead-lined coffin to be taken from Westminster to his burial place in Windsor. The procession rested overnight at Syon Abbey in present-day Middlesex, but during the night the unthinkable happened – the king's body exploded inside the coffin, and the resulting liquid leaked onto the floor of the chapel. Dogs were found licking at the mortal remains of the King of England, in fulfilment of a prophecy made by a Franciscan friar twelve years earlier.

Methods of Extraction and Processing

The earliest ore extraction methods involved open or surface mining, usually exploiting *rakes* (vertical fissures) visible on the ground. However, the presence of lead belowground produced tell-tale signs on the surface – pieces of ore turned up in ploughed land, and crops and animals performed poorly. Prospectors sank exploratory pits in likely-looking areas; some were excavated further, but many were abandoned, and the Pennine uplands are peppered with these grassy hollows.

A selection of marking hammers used to identify the mine from which the lead came

Some of the tools and equipment used in the extraction of lead ore from underground

If a promising vein was found a shallow shaft might be dug with new pits dug further along the vein. Deeper shafts were sunk in *turns* of up to 30 metres, with horizontal *galleries* between the base of one shaft and the head of the next. The miners descended and ascended using foot- and handholds carved into the shaft wall, or via *stemples* (wooden ladders). The top of the uppermost shaft usually emerged into or near a *coe* – a building used for shelter and to store tools and food.

On hillsides hushing could be used, building a temporary dam at the top of a slope and diverting rainwater and streams to gather above it. When the dam was broken a fast-flowing torrent ran down the slope, abrading away loose rock and topsoil and leaving the lead-bearing veins exposed. These were then followed into the hillside using *levels* or *adits* – horizontal or upward-sloping tunnels driven into the hill. The arched entrances to these tunnels can still be seen in many mining areas in the Dales.

The tools of the lead miner's trade were his pick, wedge, shovel and bucket or basket (*wisket* or *kibble*). This basic equipment endured from the earliest days through to the end of the industry, although it was augmented by other methods as technology advanced. Where the rock was too hard to chip or hammer, fires could be set against the walls at the end of the day and left to burn all night. In the morning the heated rock was splintered by throwing cold water at it. This was difficult and dangerous, with risks of smoke, dust and explosive fragmentation of the rock, but it was done for many hundreds of years.

Small amounts of ore could be lifted to the surface up *winding shafts*, equipped with winches, ropes and *stowes* (windlasses). Deeper shafts required horse power to lift the additional weight of ropes and equipment; horses were harnessed in *gins* or *whims* and walked in circles to raise buckets and lifts. Horse gins were also used to lift water out of flooded levels; this sometimes had to continue around the clock, with horses and men working in shifts.

Ore was also carried out along levels, long sloping tunnels that usually opened into valley bottoms. Rails might be laid for wheeled *tubs*, pushed by boys or women, and in the larger levels horses were used to draw wagons into and out of the mine.

Hydraulic pumps Sir Francis mine Swaledale

Once the ore had been brought to the surface it was dressed – broken away from waste rock, crushed by *buckers* (hammers), *buddled* (washed) if necessary, and then *jigged* (sieved) to find large lumps of *bing* (rich ore) for smelting. This was often done away from the mine itself, on a stone-flagged *dressing floor* close to sources of water (for washing and later for water power) and wood or charcoal (fuel for smelting).

Traditional smelting used a *bail* smelter, essentially a large fire on the westward side of a hill to take advantage of the prevailing wind. This technology is likely to have changed little since pre-Roman times, but bail smelters were inefficient and reliant on weather conditions, requiring two days of steady winds to maintain the high temperatures necessary for smelting. They could also only cope with large lumps of rich bing ore, meaning that poorer quality *bouse* ore accumulated in waste heaps.

Technological innovations in the sixteenth century brought water-powered bellows to heat blast furnaces, which could extract lead from smaller lumps of poorer quality ore. Old waste heaps and waste rock in exhausted workings were re-exploited; these relatively easy sources of ore provided a source of income for miners who could take advantage of the more efficient smelting technology.

Arkindale Mines Ledger, with kind permission of D. Carlisle

The seventeenth century saw the advent of gunpowder blasting, and mechanical rock borers arrived in Yorkshire in the nineteenth century, although traditional pick-and-hammer mining still remained common. Improvements in drainage techniques meant that mines could be driven ever deeper; waterwheels were used to drive pumps, with complicated systems of reservoirs and watercourses on the surface to ensure a good head of water year-round, even in areas with no natural water supply.

The old smelting mills had many problems – blast furnaces were prone to overheating and had to be shut down at the end of each day, and frequent repairs were needed. Water-powered smelters were restricted to riverside sites, and they required a steady supply of wood. By the eighteenth century timber supplies were running out and coke or coal had to be used instead, but this introduced impurities into the lead.

New reverberatory or cupola furnaces were introduced around 1737, superseding the older blast furnaces. The new design separated the fuel and source of heat from the ore, reducing contamination and meaning that coal could be used. They could be operated continuously, they produced less pollution, no water power was needed, and many later furnaces had long horizontal or uphill flues to condense fumes before they were discharged through a tall chimney. In Yorkshire these flues were very long and straight, sometimes running for up to a kilometre, and many contained condensing chambers from which sweepings could be collected. These contained solidified metal which could be re-smelted, making the technology even more efficient.

Fortunes were sometimes made during this time, but as mines were sunk ever deeper, water and good air became crucial issues, and crippling pumping, ventilation and operational costs meant that many mines became financially unviable. Ownership disputes over veins were common, sometimes rumbling on for decades with no resolution.

The work of a lead miner was difficult and dangerous, both above and below ground. Miners typically worked six-hour shifts rather than the eight hours or even longer in other industries, reflecting the punishing labour but also the fact that most miners also operated smallholdings to supplement their diets and incomes, and needed some waking hours to devote to this. They often had to walk long distances to reach the mine, and they might also have to descend shafts and travel long distances underground to reach their working area. In the winter months miners often went for days on end without seeing daylight.

Lead is poisonous to animals and plants, and significant levels of pollution occurred at the mines themselves as well as around smelting and processing sites. The sites of some bail smelters are still bare of vegetation to this day, as are the gashes left in hillsides by hushing, and land polluted by lead-mining activities was avoided by farmers. However, problems still occurred, and many legal cases were brought against mine owners by farmers whose livestock and crops were sick or failing.

Miners and their families also suffered ill-effects. As well as the toxic effects of the lead itself and the pollution from smelting, miners worked in constant physical danger because of cave-ins, collapses and suffocation due to poor ventilation, as well as the endemic lung diseases caused by dust from chipping, crushing and blasting. The average life expectancy of a lead miner was around fifty years.

The industry went into decline in the late eighteenth century because of worked-out veins, increased costs, and cheap imported supplies of lead after import duties were abolished in 1845. The industry struggled on as long as it could, but by 1914 the ancient lead mining way of life in the Yorkshire Dales had all but died out.

Right: Surrender Smelt Mill

Lead Mining Sites in the Dales

The Yorkshire Dales are rich in industrial remains connected with lead mining. Many of the above-ground buildings in the Dales were dismantled in the century after they fell idle, with the dressed stone being reused by the ever-practical local population; the chapel in the village of Muker was constructed out of stone from the Old Gang Smelt Mill buildings. However, many buildings remain, either as ruins or having been restored and preserved. This section will take you on a brief tour of some of the most significant and scenic.

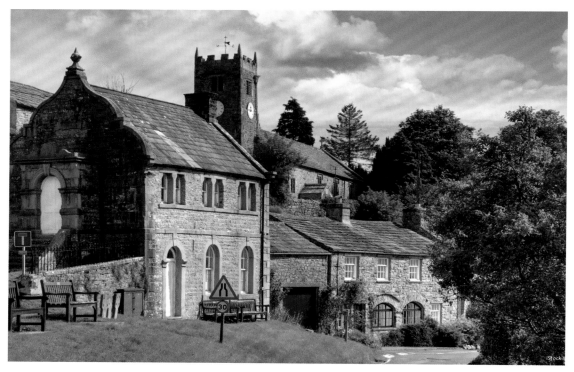

Muker chapel, built with stone from the Old Gang Smelt Mill

Swaledale was one of the busiest and most productive lead mining areas in the Pennines. The steep valley sides meant that hushing was the predominant technique for exposing ore; Gunnerside Gill was the site of repeated hushing, with three great hushes (Bunton, Friarfold and Gorton) still bare of vegetation.

Levels were driven into hillsides where ore was exposed. The Sir Francis Level in Gunnerside was begun in 1864 to reach the Swaledale end of the Friarfold vein, with ore taken to the Old Gang and Surrender smelt mills. There is a ruined wheel pit on the surface here with extensive remains below ground as well, although access to these is only possible for expert cavers. Hard Level was driven later as a cheaper and easier option than transporting ore over the hilltops.

The dressing floor at Sir Francis Mine, Gunnerside

Hushes in Gunnerside Gill

Sir Francis Mine closed in 1882 during a slump in lead prices; it later reopened, but during the hiatus many levels had flooded and most of the equipment and machinery were water-damaged. The mine never made a profit again, and closed permanently soon after.

The Beldi Hill mines were near Keld and Swinner Gill in upper Swaledale. The Beldi Hill Mill once housed three furnaces and a roasting oven for resmelting slag. Beldi Hill was also the site of a series of quarrels between Lord Pomfret (of the prosperous Wharton family) and the Parkes company about rights to use a level for access to workings. One side dug shafts while the other filled them in, and fights broke out underground; the lawyers were kept busy for years.

Arkengarthdale is a side-valley off Swaledale, and mines here also exploited the Friarfold vein. The Arkengarthdale mines were owned by the Bathurst family; Charles Bathurst lent his initials to a mine and a couple of local inns. The village of Reeth stands centrally between Swaledale and Arkengarthdale, once an important hub and effectively the mining capital of the northern ore fields.

The Octagon Mill, built near Langthwaite in 1804, was the largest in the Dales. It had six ore hearths and a ten-metre waterwheel, although now reduced to its foundations. There is an extensive double flue still visible, along with hushes and spoil heaps. A hexagonal powder house also stands in a nearby field, once used for the secure storage of black powder for blasting. Powder houses were always safely distant from mines, smelt mills and any potential sources of sparks or heat.

Reeth village, with pits and spoil heaps visible in the landscape

Furnace vents inside Grinton Smelt Mill

Buildings at the Old Gang site

Grinton Smelt Mill served the mines of Swaledale, and was preserved and restored by the Yorkshire Dales National Park in the 1980s. The extant buildings date from the 1820s, but lead was worked on this site from at least 1733. The mill stands on a level site with a good supply of water, and the main building once contained two furnaces. The tuyère vents for the bellows can still be seen.

The Old Gang and Surrender mills are in a remote valley between Arkengarthdale and Swaledale. Surrender had four hearths, a flue stretching up the hillside, and a waterwheel to power the bellows; it closed in 1881. Old Gang was around a mile away, by Old Gang Beck. Old Gang forms an impressive group of ruins, with four hearths and four flues joining to form one large flue stretching up the hillside. Uphill from the main buildings was a long narrow subdivided building (now without its roof); this was the peat store, which once housed a year's worth of peat to fuel the furnaces.

Nearby are the stone-flagged dressing floor and the entrances to Hard Level and Spence Level, which joined with mines working several veins. Indeed, mining in Swaledale was so extensive, and levels were driven with such purpose and accuracy, that it was once possible to enter Sir Francis Mine in Gunnerside Gill and follow a complex underground route to emerge at Moulds Level in Arkengarthdale, six miles away.

The close proximity and extent of the underground workings in the Dales sometimes led to disputes and even disaster. Miners often broke through into each other's tunnels; sometimes this was amicable, but sometimes not, as in the dispute between the Parkes and Wharton companies at Beldi Hill. More tragically, a group of miners once broke through into a flooded level in another mine and had to flee for their lives, and it is said that the Water Blast Vein in Arkengarthdale got its name when a group of eighteenth-century miners breached the wall of an underground lake. Twenty-four miners and two ponies were washed from the mine in the ensuing deluge and lost their lives; eighteen of the men were from the tiny mining hamlet of Booze. The effects of this terrible loss of life and livelihood on the local community can only be imagined.

Chimney on Grassington Moor

Another significant group of mines was on Grassington Moor, exploiting the Bycliff vein. This is a very different site from Swaledale – there are no steep valleys, which meant no hushing and more use of bell pits and shafts. Mining has a long history around Grassington; the monks of Fountains Abbey once worked a smelt mill here, but since the end of the eighteenth century the area has been associated with the Dukes of Devonshire. They employed a local agent around 1790 who engineered a drainage tunnel (Duke's Level) to revitalise previously flooded and worked-out shafts and allow deeper working.

The New Road was also built to allow easier transport of ore, along with mine offices at Yarnbury. All this investment paid off; Chatsworth House in Derbyshire, the spectacular Devonshire family seat, was built with profits from lead-mining investments at Grassington. The Grassington mines had what was effectively their own 'lead wharf' at Gargrave on the Leeds-Liverpool canal, for the transport of lead to the industrial centres and ports.

Peak production at Grassington was during the 1850s and 1860s, but it dropped away rapidly and the last mine ceased production in 1877. The smelt mills continued a short while longer, with the final load of ore smelted in 1882. There are many remains on the moor, with shafts, bell pits, bouseteams, a long straight flue from the cupola smelt mill, and not least the tall flue chimney, carefully restored in 1971 by Earby Mines Research Group.

Out and About in Lead Mining Country

Belying the region's busy industrial past, the Yorkshire Dales contain some of the most beautiful countryside in England. The Yorkshire Dales National Park, created in 1954, consists of a string of stunning valleys divided by high and lonely moorland, all criss-crossed with trails, bridleways and waymarked public footpaths.

This section of the book offers two walks in Swaledale, both suitable for families and the reasonably fit, which will take you deep into lead-mining country in the Yorkshire Dales. As with any outdoor activity, before you set out please make certain you are physically able and confident of the route, always take account of the weather, and make sure you have planned refreshment stops or you are carrying enough food and drink for the day.

Additionally, while they are fascinating, industrial remains can also be dangerous. Do not climb on ruined structures or machinery, and on no account enter underground workings. Timber props and platforms may look reliable, but they are certain to be old and rotten, and the movements of earth and water over the centuries can render even the most solid stonework liable to collapse with no warning.

Grassington Moor

Walk 1: Upper Swaledale

About the area

Upper Swaledale is Dales country at its finest, a particularly remote area where old haybarns are dotted about flower-bedecked summer meadows. At its peak lead mining completely dominated this area, and the haunting remains of old mines, smelting mills and associated workings are scattered about the landscape.

Muker is a good centre for exploring the upper dale, with the Farmer's Arms and a shop/tearoom. This is probably the most picturesque village in the dale, with a fine grouping of buildings rising above the beck. St Mary's Church was first built in 1580, although the present structure dates largely from 1890. The Literary Institute of 1868 is prominent in front of it. The old school is now a crafts shop and gallery, and tablets proclaim that the famous Kearton brothers of neighbouring Thwaite were former pupils. They went on to become pioneers in the early days of nature photography.

Thwaite is a tiny village that must be a welcome sight to walkers on the Pennine Way, who descend to it from the long, lonely miles of Great Shunner Fell. The long-established Kearton Country Hotel is a friendly place for refreshment.

Your routes between the two villages vary immensely. The outward leg via Muker Side enjoys magnificent views across the valley to Kisdon, while beyond Muker the Swale Gorge is backed by the moorland heights of Rogan's Seat, with the mighty bulk of Great Shunner Fell straight ahead. The return walk is a contrastingly easy stroll through archetypal Swaledale meadows punctuated by a string of old wall-stiles.

iStock

THE BASICS

Distance: 3½ miles (5.6 kilometres)

Gradient: One sustained climb of around 425ft/130m, otherwise flat

Severity: Easy after the first uphill mile

Approx. time to walk: 2 to 2½ hours

Stiles: 14 (though some are simple gaps)

Maps: OS Landranger 98 Wensleydale and Upper Wharfedale; Explorer OL30 Yorkshire Dales North/Central

Path description: A stony track followed by field paths

Start point: Muker village centre (GR SD 910978)

Parking: Village car park

Dog friendly: Sheep pastures, dogs on leads please

Public toilets: At start

Nearest food: Pub and tearoom at start; refreshments at Thwaite

The walk

1. Cross the bridge at the east end of the village and leave the road immediately after the car park by an enclosed track rising to the right. Beyond some barns it crosses a small stream and doubles back to climb towards Muker Side. Ultimately the way swings left to rise to a T-junction of walled tracks at Three Loaning End (*loaning* is a local dialect word for lane).

2. Go right and follow a near-level path along Muker Side. Just after bridging a tiny stream, turn right down a walled, part-grassy way as far as a tiny barn on a bend. Here, leave by a gate on the left and follow a nice little path, crossing a field-bottom to become briefly enclosed before merging into a descending track above the house at Appletree Thwaite.

3. Go through a gate at the end, and follow the track down through a further gate and down a larger field. At the bottom, locate a stile in the wall just to the right of the track. This gives a tiny short-cut over a little stone-arched footbridge over Cliff Beck in a lovely little ravine.

4. The now-enclosed track is rejoined just beyond, running out onto the valley road. Turn left past the Hawes junction to drop down into Thwaite, crossing Thwaite Bridge to enter the village.

5. Turn along the short lane in front of the Kearton Country Hotel, and at the end, as the lane swings right, a Pennine Way sign points you along a short enclosed path just right of a farmyard. Two stiles in quick succession lead into a field. Here the Pennine Way strikes left, but you continue with Thwaite Beck to a wall-stile ahead. Here, leave the beck on a narrow path across three further fields, in the second of which you follow a wall. At the end you converge with a smaller beck, Skeb Skeugh, coming in from the left. It is crossed on a stone-arched footbridge.

6. From a stile just beyond the bridge, follow a wall to a corner stile at the end, then pass right of a barn to a wall-stile, from where a beckside path joins the road at Usha Gap Bridge. Go briefly left along the road, and then go left to the farmhouse at Usha Gap.

7. Turn right through the farmyard to a gate into a camping field, then bear left to find a wall-stile near the far end. From here, follow a string of obvious wall-stiles along a faint path across the field-bottoms to Muker. In the final field the path is flagged. Emerging into the village, a little pathway on the right drops down to emerge alongside the pub.

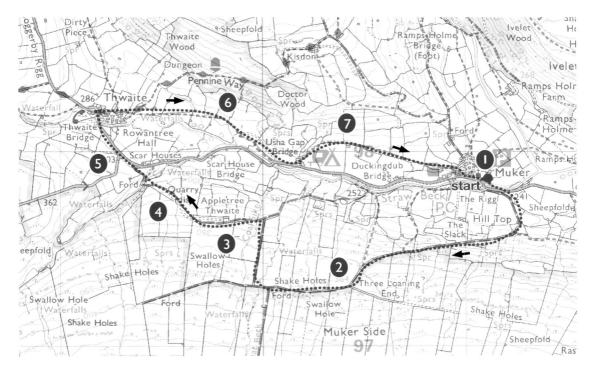

Walk 2: Around Reeth

About the area

Swaledale is at its most colourful and vibrant around Reeth, where the major side valley of Arkengarthdale joins the Swale in the shadow of the long, high skyline of Fremington Edge. Additionally, Harkerside Moor dominates the main dale across the river.

Reeth was a focal point for the lead mining industry in Swaledale, and was once much more populous. It boasts an enviable position on the slopes of Calver Hill, well above the confluence of the Swale and Arkle Beck. The large central village green is surrounded by inns, shops and tearooms as well as a National Park Centre, and there is also a folk museum. Parking can be an issue around the green in summer, particularly when market traders set up stalls on Fridays.

Grinton is the only settlement of any size on the south bank of the Swale, and was once the major centre for the dale above Richmond. At its heart are its pub, church, and a Literary Institute of 1903. St Andrew's is known as the 'Cathedral of the Dales' because of its size; its parish once extended through the entire valley as far as the Westmorland border. Between the church and the river is Blackburn Hall, a manor house with sections believed to be much older than its 1635 datestone.

Either side of Grinton the Swale is a delight to follow, with easy riverside paths. The tiny settlement of Fremington is divided into two halves: Low Fremington is by the main road, while High Fremington is a haphazard grouping of dwellings with enviable privacy linked by a network of narrow byways.

THE BASICS

Distance: 3½ miles (5.6 kilometres)

Gradient: Mostly level

Severity: Very easy

Approx time to walk: 2 to 2½ hours

Stiles: 8

Maps: OS Landranger 98 Wensleydale & Upper Wharfedale; Explorer OL30 Yorkshire Dales North/Central

Path description: Riverbank and fieldpaths

Start point: Reeth village centre (GR SE 038992)

Parking: Roadside parking in village centre

Dog friendly: Sheep pastures, dogs on leads please

Public toilets: At start and in Grinton

Nearest food: Pubs and cafés at start; pub in Grinton

The walk

1. From the green in Reeth, pass along the front of the King's Arms and the Black Bull to a tiny green at Anvil Square. Across it, set back to the right, a 'to the river' sign sends a path off between walls. Follow this to emerge onto a narrow road; go left to join a suburban street. Turn left to a T-junction, then right along a narrow lane past the surgery, with a stone-flagged pathway alongside the road. At the end, turn left down an enclosed footway to emerge at a gate overlooking the river. The path bears right through two fields to a suspension footbridge across the Swale.

2. Across the river, turn downstream on a grassy bank which diverts from the river's course. At a corner, turn left on a grassy bridleway that passes through a gate, then along to a corner gate where it becomes enclosed. After a slight rise this splendid enclosed way runs on for some time before being rejoined by the Swale. The river soon veers off again, and the path resumes its enclosed course by bearing right to a gate onto a back road.

3. Go left towards Grinton for a short distance, and after the church tower appears, go through a gap on the left to follow a path down a few steps to the riverbank. A short riverside stroll passes the churchyard, which can be accessed part-way along, or simply remain on the broad access road past Blackburn Hall to emerge into the village centre opposite the Bridge Inn.

4. Go left to cross the bridge, then turn downstream on a path along the wooded riverbank to emerge into open pasture. At the other end a wooded bank forces the path up to a stile onto the Marrick Priory access road. Turn left to meet a through-road, and then right for a short uphill stretch to a gap-stile on the left, just before a driveway at a bend.

5. Cross to a stile in the left corner ahead, then follow a sturdy wall until you pass through a gate to its other side. Resume through two further gates to follow a fence above Sorrel Sykes farm to reach an enclosed way. Ignore this and go through a gate in front; a wallside path crosses a field-top to a small gate onto an enclosed footway on the edge of Fremington. Head straight along the path onto a narrow lane, following it left and then first right.

6. The lane quickly swings left to drop steeply away. Here, go straight along a short track to a gate into a field. Reeth appears under Calver Hill just ahead. The track soon bears right, but instead follow a path tracing the left-hand wall down to a corner stile, then down again to a stile in your wall. Aiming for Reeth Bridge, cross the field to a gate, with another just beyond it bringing you onto the road at the bridge on Arkle Beck. Cross it to re-enter the village, and continue on past a corner shop to rise back onto the green.

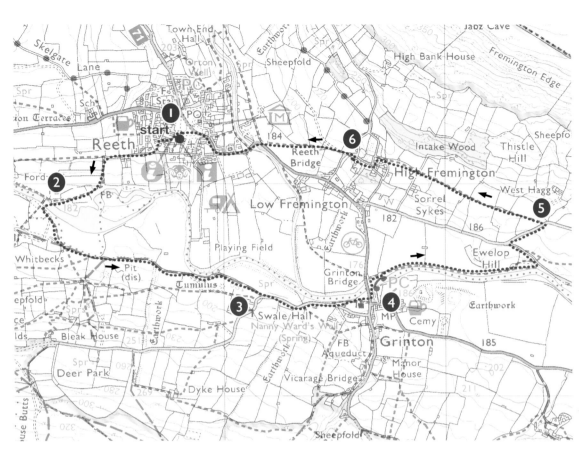

You might be interested in other Yorkshire books from Bradwell Books

Walks for all Ages West Yorkshire

Walks for all Ages Yorkshire Dales

Walks for all Ages North York Moors

Walks for all Ages South Yorkshire

Bradwell's Longer Walks in the Yorkshire Dales

Bradwell's Pocket Walking Guide to The Yorkshire Dales

Bradwell's Family Cycle Rides Yorkshire

Yorkshire Dialect

Yorkshire Ghost Stories

Bradwell's Images of The Yorkshire Dales

Bradwell's Images of the North York Moors

Yorkshire Murder Stories

Bradwell's Book of Yorkshire Wit & Humour

Legends & Folklore Yorkshire

Colour Yorkshire

Available from your local bookshop or order online
bradwellbooks.co.uk